Spot the Crook
A Search-and-Find Book

HELP US FIND
THIS NAUGHTY CROOK! HE ALWAYS
WEARS A RED SCARF AS A GOOD LUCK CHARM,
SO WE CALL HIM
THE RED SCARF CROOK!

POLICE PARADE

The police are marching proudly through the LEGO® CITY park, but they never take their eyes off the crowds in their hunt for the notorious Red Scarf Crook. Can you find him, too?

Have you spotted the crook? Well done! The police have another task for you. There are ten differences between this picture and the one on the previous page. Can you find them all?

AT THE GARAGE

Need your car fixed? Got a flat tyre? The car mechanics at the LEGO® CITY garage can solve your problems in no time! Well, it can take a bit longer on a day like this – phew, it's so busy! Can you help ease the load by finding the Red Scarf Crook in the crowd?

SCULPTURE CONTEST

Artists look forward all year to the Annual LEGO® CITY Sculpture Contest – and art lovers flock from miles around to see the amazing statues! Can you spot the Red Scarf Crook causing mischief?

You found him again! Wow!
It's time for another challenge, then.
Look carefully at this picture
and try to find ten tiny differences
from the first image.

CONSTRUCTION SITE

The industrious construction workers are busy building an amazing new shopping mall in LEGO® CITY. But the bustling construction site is the perfect place for the Red Scarf Crook to hide! Can you spot him before he runs away again?

COSTUME BALL

Where can you meet an astronaut, a cowboy and a pharaoh at the same time? At a LEGO® CITY costume ball, of course! What would you wear if you joined in the fun? And can you spot the Red Scarf Crook hiding among the guests?

Did you spot him? Well done! Now, have a closer look at this picture – it looks the same as the first, but it's not! Can you spot the ten differences between them?

TRAIN STATION

It's just another normal, busy day at the LEGO® CITY train station. Passengers are waiting to board, new tracks are being laid and... the police are chasing crooks! Quick, can you help them find the Red Scarf Crook before he escapes on a train?

A DAY AT THE BEACH

Bright sun, white sand and crystal-clear water – what more do you need on your day off? The beach is looking a little crowded though – perfect for pesky crooks who like to hide! Can you find our naughty crook on the beach?

You did it! Fantastic!
Now, with your keen eyes,
you'll have no problem spotting
ten differences between the two images!

FIRE!

The pizzeria is on fire! But don't panic!
The LEGO® CITY fire fighters are already
handling the situation. They are the best
of the best and they know what to do.
You focus on finding the Red Scarf Crook!

CITY SQUARE

Wondering what to do on a lazy afternoon?
Come to the LEGO® CITY square, where
there's always something going on!
You can listen to music, watch the street
performers, sit by the fountain…
Or look for the Red Scarf Crook!

Awesome! You seem to be a real expert at spotting our troublesome crook. Now, do you think you can find ten differences between this picture and the first?

POLICE STATION

High alert at the LEGO® CITY police station! There's been a prison break and the police need to get all the escaped criminals back behind bars. Can you help them by spotting the Red Scarf Crook?

PN 7288

CONCERT IN THE PARK

Do you like music? Good, because the biggest pop stars in LEGO® CITY are singing at the park today! Be careful, though – the biggest star of the criminal world is there, too! Can you spot the Red Scarf Crook hiding in the crowds?

Once you've found the crook, can you spot ten more details that make this picture different from the first?

There are still plenty of fun things to find in this book!
Can you spot everything on these lists?

AT THE GARAGE

- [ ] a policeman with binoculars
- [ ] a mechanic with a sausage
- [ ] two cows
- [ ] a policeman with handcuffs
- [ ] a blond surfer
- [ ] a sleeping construction worker
- [ ] a man in a canoe
- [ ] a man talking on his mobile phone
- [ ] four dogs
- [ ] a detective with a magnifying glass

CONSTRUCTION SITE

- [ ] a white cat
- [ ] a cook
- [ ] three walkie-talkies
- [ ] a man with binoculars
- [ ] a bucket of white paint
- [ ] two traffic cones
- [ ] two banana skins
- [ ] a checked flag
- [ ] a lady with a blue bag
- [ ] a policeman with handcuffs

TRAIN STATION

- [ ] two men shaking hands
- [ ] a yawning boy
- [ ] a crook with a ladder
- [ ] an artist with his painting
- [ ] a fire fighter with a red hose
- [ ] a crook with a broom
- [ ] a sleeping farmer with a beard
- [ ] four photographers
- [ ] big blue ear-phones
- [ ] a train mechanic riding on a bull

FIRE!

- [ ] eight pizzas
- [ ] a policeman looking for his dog
- [ ] a mechanic with a black wrench
- [ ] a pizza delivery boy
- [ ] a photographer
- [ ] two red bicycles
- [ ] a fire fighter with foam on his face
- [ ] six brown suitcases
- [ ] two fire fighters with walkie-talkies
- [ ] three fish

POLICE STATION

- [ ] three police motorbikes
- [ ] a photographer with blond hair
- [ ] a crook with a crowbar
- [ ] a TV cameraman
- [ ] a brown horse
- [ ] a policewoman on a bicycle
- [ ] three magnifying glasses
- [ ] a policeman wearing a white helmet
- [ ] three lollipops
- [ ] six crooks with big brown sacks